WHAT BABIES DO:

The
SECRET THOUGHTS
of
BABIES

Waaaaaaaaaaaa...

Steven Appleby

First published in 1996

Copyright Steven Appleby © 1996

The moral right of the author
has been asserted blah, blah blah...

Bloomsbury Publishing Plc
2 Soho Square, London W1V 6HB

ISBN 0 7475 2972 8

Printed in Great Britain by
St Edmundsbury Press, Suffolk

FOR JASPER

THE COMPLETE
NEW-BORN BABY
RANGE OF ACTIVITY:

Asleep.

Awake.

Eating.

Waaaaa...

Cross.

Not cross.
(NB - Babies are never
happy. Just not cross).

Filling a nappy.

Hungry.

Windy.

A BABY'S ABILITY TO EMPATHISE WITH OTHER LIVING CREATURES:

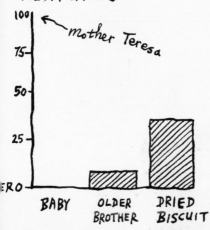

100
← mother Teresa

75

50

25

ZERO

BABY　　OLDER BROTHER　　DRIED BISCUIT

SOME ADVICE ~
ALWAYS SUPPORT YOUR
BABY'S HEAD...

OR THIS WILL HAPPEN.

THOUGHTS AT 3 ~ 4 WEEKS

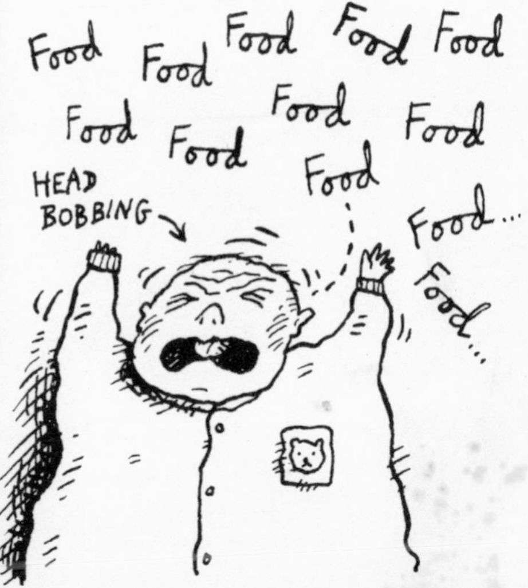

HOW BABIES SEE THE WORLD

fig a~

fig 6~

fig c –

4 - 10 WEEKS

onfusion...
Surprise...
Puzzled...
Not understanding...
Perplexed...
Bewilderment...
Mixed up...
hat's
hat?..
What's going on?...

THE MODERN, ENLIGHTENED ATTITUDE:

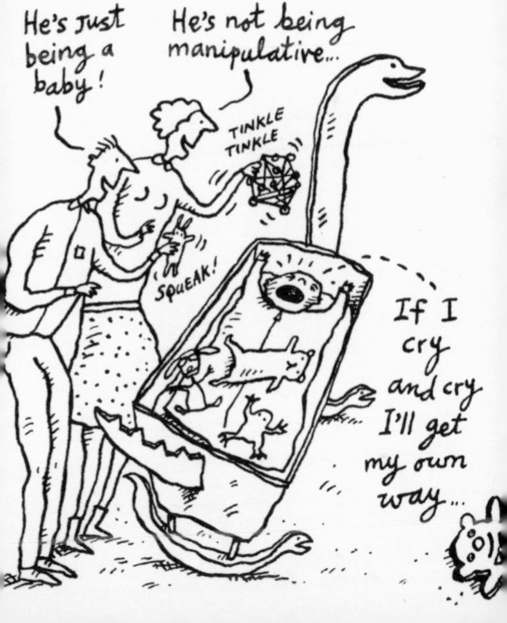

Not having their
nappy changed.

Being dressed.

Being undressed.

THINGS THAT MAKE
BABIES HAPPY...

Food.

Being asleep.

No clothes on at all.

SOME BABY THOUGHTS

Goo.

"In a moment ..."

" ... for no particular reason, I am going to throw my arms and legs in the air and scream and scream and scream.

"I'm unhappy so I
want you to be
unhappy too."

Waaaaaa....

"I won't go to sleep here..."

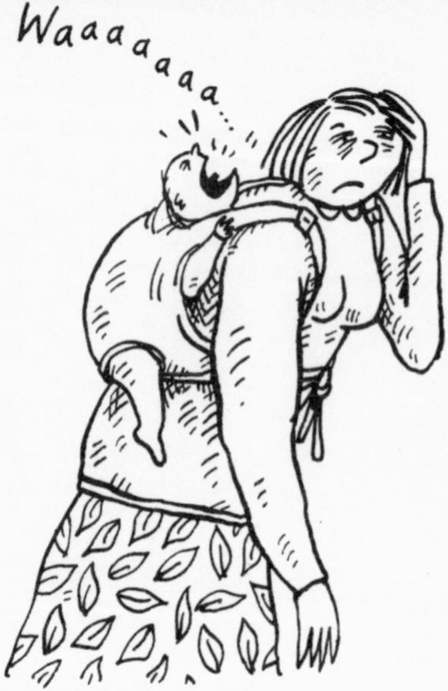

"or here..."

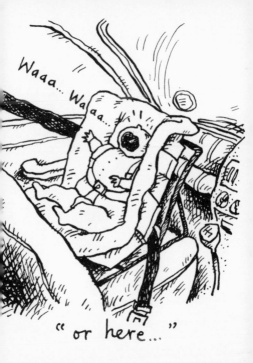

"or here..."

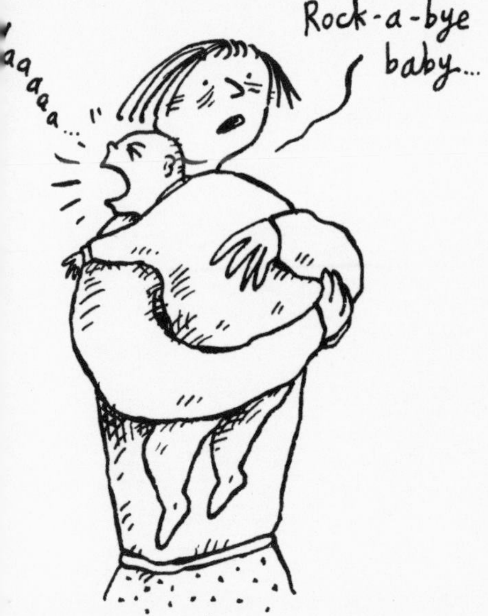

"or here..."

THEY SLEEP DURING THE DAY SO THEY CAN STAY AWAKE ALL NIGHT!

"I have filled my napp
with green slime."

Un goo.

"The parent name I learn to say first is the one I love most"

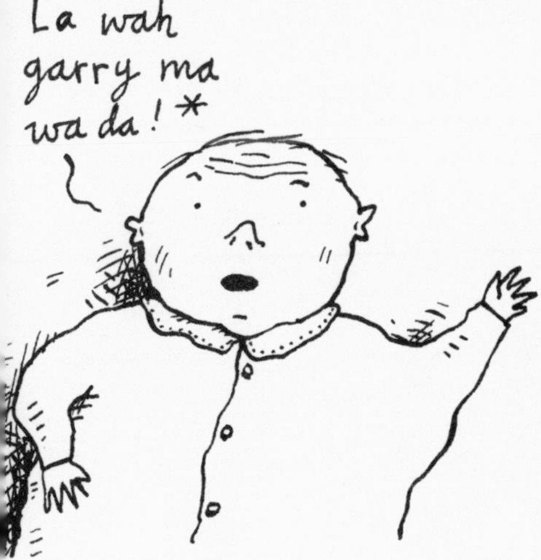

* "Am I adopted?"

"I am about to be sick."

"Am I the Meaning of Life?.."

IT IS HARD TO BELIEVE,
BUT ONE DAY YOUR BABY
WILL GROW UP...